THE
WELCOMING DOOR

Parables of the Carpenter
Volume One

THE
WELCOMING DOOR

KENNY KEMP

Alta Films
PRESS
SAN DIEGO

THE WELCOMING DOOR

Alta Films Press books may be purchased for educational,
business, or sales promotional use. For information,
contact Alta Films Press, 627 9th Street, Ramona, CA 92065.

PAPERBACK EDITION
Designed by Bonnie Sheets & Kenny Kemp
Cover paintings and interior tool icons by J. Kirk Richards
Frontispiece by Kenny Kemp

Library of Congress Cataloging-in-Publication Data

Kemp, Kenny.
The welcoming door / Kenny Kemp.
p. cm.
ISBN-13: 978-1-892442-26-4 (paperback)
1. Jesus Christ—Fiction. 2. Bible—N.T.—History of Biblical events—
Fiction. 3. Biographical fiction. 4. Christian fiction. I. Title.
PS3561.E39922W45 2008
813'.54—dc21

02 03 04 05 06 07 08 09 10

www.kennykemp.com   PRINTED IN U.S.A.

Alta Films
PRESS

*And with such parables spake he the word
unto them, as they were able to hear it.
— Mark 4;33*

AN OBSCURE PROVINCE

O n the shore of the Middle Sea, at the far eastern reach of the Roman Empire, a small nation strains under the yoke of bondage. Its people, long of history and patience, look to the past for their future, prophecies of a day when God will raise up a man to liberate them from their oppressors. A messiah.

Most people of this small nation live within a day's ride of Jerusalem, the city created by the great warrior-king David. Jerusalem sits on a wedge-shaped plateau between two steep valleys, protected by watchtowers guarding the approach from the north. Hundreds of years ago, the Babylonians laid siege to the city, and from then until now, a succession of foreign armies has assaulted it. And when the great Roman general Pompey entered the Holy of Holies in the Temple, their freedom came to an end.

To the north, in the green hills that roll between

the Middle Sea and the lake called Galilee, worlds collide more peacefully. Trade routes make distant peoples partners, travelers acquaintances, and strangers friends. The people of Galilee work fields of barley and wheat, harvest sweet figs and savory olives, fish in the clear waters of the Galilee, and live in harmony with Assyrian, Phoenician, and Roman alike.

Rome, for the most part, grants its subjects religious freedom. Roman gods are plentiful, so there is no fear that they will be eclipsed by the Jewish god. But though they are benign in spiritual matters, the Romans are exacting in temporal ones. Heavy taxes are borne by all their subjects, and to the Jews in Jerusalem who watch the Roman legions circle the Temple on holy days, Rome is a brutal oppressor. To the Galileans, Rome's presence is not so onerous. Yet still they yearn for freedom, and so their hearts often turn to the prophecies of the Messiah.

A few miles south of Sepphoris, the seat of Roman government in Galilee, lies Nazareth, a small village overlooking the fertile Jezreel Valley. Fewer than twenty families live here, working the trades and crafts, tilling the soil, and tending livestock. In a small carpentry shop works a man named Joseph bar Jacob. When his eldest son was born in Bethlehem during a census journey, a marvelous star led shepherds and royalty alike to the manger where the child lay. And after, warned by an angel that King Herod was seeking the child's life, Joseph and Mary fled to Egypt and lived in the shadow of pyramids and strange gods. There Joseph worked in his trade, and the boy grew. When news of Herod's death reached him, Joseph brought his family home.

Now, many years later, the boy has grown into a man and works alongside Joseph, cutting and sanding and varnishing wood; building tables and chairs and houses; chiseling and fitting stone; and digging culverts and wells.

Joseph watches Jeshua work and remembers the portentous words of the angel who foretold his birth: "He shall save the people from their sins." If the scribes and rabbis are right, those same gentle hands that work the wood so tenderly now will someday be required to take up the sword.

Jeshua looks up from the chair leg he is planing. He sees the dark look on his father's face and asks, "What is it?"

"Nothing," says Joseph. "Just worrying."

Jeshua looks at his father in that piercing way Joseph has never gotten used to. Jeshua holds the chair leg up for his father to see. "Don't worry," he says, smiling. "I know what I'm doing."

Joseph sees the strength and kindness and wisdom in the young man's eyes. "Yes," he says, nodding. "I can see that you do."

ONE

AN UNEXPECTED VISITOR

Jeshua bar Joseph stopped at the gate and set his wooden toolbox on the low stone wall that surrounded the large dooryard. He straightened and stretched. His back ached. It was hot, even though it was early, and he was tired, having walked several miles this morning.

A servant boy came running out of the house, his sandals slapping on the hard dirt. He ran quickly, waving at Jeshua, excitement on his face. As he drew closer, he stopped abruptly, and the excitement disappeared.

"Oh. I thought you were someone else," he said, and turned back to the house.

"Who was I supposed to be?" asked Jeshua. The boy didn't answer; he was already halfway across the dooryard.

Jeshua stepped through the gate, which was topped by a curved trellis upon which spring's first green grape leaves were sprouting. He surveyed the house. It was made of limestone, large and solid, with big windows draped in fine, colorful tapestries to keep out the heat. The walls were plastered tan stucco; it was no doubt cool inside. The sloping roof was made of sturdy brown tiles. The well just inside the gate reminded him of his parched throat. He would like a drink, but it would be rude to help himself before being invited to do so.

The boy disappeared inside, and the heavy oak door thudded closed behind him. Jeshua walked across the dooryard and examined the door. It was thick and dark, the varnish long since worn off. The red leather hinges were worn and sagging, one nearly torn in two. The door handle was rusty black iron, worn smooth and bent with use.

Just then the door opened. Jeshua had to take a step back as it swung outward, creaking loudly. Before him stood an imposing old man with a full gray beard. He wore a gray knee-length tunic and a wide leather belt. His eyes were dark and his fists were clenched on his hips. "What are you doing inside the dooryard?" he boomed. He slammed the door shut behind him.

"Peace be unto you. I am Jeshua bar Joseph. Of Nazareth."

"Jeshua bar Joseph?"

"You asked me to come."

"I did?" asked the old man, his eyes scanning the horizon beyond Jeshua.

"To fix the door," said Jeshua, pointing at his toolbox.

"What door?" asked the man. Then suddenly his eyes opened wide. "Aah! You're the carpenter!"

Jeshua nodded.

The old man extended a huge hand, taking Jeshua's and pumping it vigorously. "Yes, yes! The door!" He gestured at the road beyond the stone wall. "I'm sorry. We were expecting someone else."

Jeshua nodded. "Who?"

The old man looked thoughtfully at Jeshua for a long moment, then said, "You are a journeyman . . . ah . . ."

"Jeshua. Yes, I am."

"Jeshua. Of Nazareth. A journeyman," said the old man absently, as if cataloging the facts for later use. "I am Eli and this is my home. From now on, you will ask permission before entering the dooryard, is that clear?"

Jeshua nodded. "Yes. My apologies."

The old man studied Jeshua, sizing him up. "Well," he said, standing aside and gesturing at the door. "Here it is. In bad need of repair, don't you think?"

Jeshua took a step past the old man to get a closer look. He nodded. "Yes, it is old and nearly worn out."

Behind him, Eli harrumphed. "Like me."

Jeshua smiled to himself as he examined the door, running his hands over the wood. "But it is of fine quality and has aged well." He straightened and turned to Eli, who was again looking at the road, which disappeared over the green rolling hills of Galilee. "Like you," Jeshua said quietly.

Eli turned. His brow was furrowed. He pointed at the door. "Can it be saved?"

Jeshua nodded. "It must be taken apart, planed, refinished—"

"How much?" queried the old man crossly.

Jeshua was examining the leather hinges and felt the question like a hard jab in the ribs. He turned to face Eli. "As was agreed, sir. No more."

Eli frowned. "And certainly no less, I'm sure." He pushed past Jeshua, pulled the door open, and strode inside. "To work, then, young man," he said, and the door creaked shut behind him.

TWO

Master of the Universe

Jeshua turned to his donkey and began unloading his tools and sawhorses. The same young boy who thought he was someone else was drawing water from the well, watching him out of the corner of his eye. Jeshua smiled. "Peace be unto you," he said, leading the donkey over.

"And unto you, peace," said the boy tentatively.

"What is your name?"

"Arah," said the boy, his eyes suspicious but interested.

"I like that name," said Jeshua. "It means 'wayfarer.' Have you come far, Arah?"

The boy gave Jeshua a perplexed look. "Only from my house, over there." He pointed to a group of small wooden buildings behind the main house. "What does 'wayfarer' mean?"

"One who travels or wanders. Also a seeker of knowledge."

Arah smiled. "The only thing I seek is a full waterskin." He hauled the skin over the stone edge of the well and poured it into a large brown clay urn.

"When I'm thirsty, that's what I seek as well," hinted Jeshua, his tongue still dusty. "You have an important job, Arah."

"Tell that to the others," said the boy, tossing the waterskin back into the well.

"My name is Jeshua. I'm here to work on Master Eli's door."

"I know," said Arah, hauling the skin back up. "I saw you come."

"So you did," said Jeshua. "I'll bet you see everything here."

Arah nodded. "I do. I see everything."

"Hmm," said Jeshua, running his hand through his donkey's tangled mane.

Arah's face lit up. "Would you like to water your donkey?"

Jeshua nodded and smiled. "You are observant, Arah. That's exactly what I was going to ask."

Arah gestured to the side of the house. "There is a trough back there. Your donkey looks tired. And thirsty."

Jeshua patted the donkey on the withers. "Yes. Probably both. He is a hard worker. Like you, Arah." The boy blushed. "Hard work is a gift," said Jeshua as he led the donkey around the side of the house.

Arah followed Jeshua, lugging the sloshing water urn. He shook his head. "A gift?" He laughed.

Jeshua looked back over his shoulder. "Absolutely. From our Heavenly Father."

"Who?"

"The Master of the Universe. He is also our father."

"I never heard that," said Arah. "I know he created us, and is our Lord and we his subjects, but how is he our father?"

They stopped at the trough. Arah lifted the urn. The cool clear water splashed into the stone basin, and the donkey began to drink noisily. Jeshua turned to the boy. "Think about it. What kind of things does a father do for his children?"

They began to walk back toward the well. Arah carried the urn, thinking hard. His face lit up. "A father feeds his children and gives them shelter. He teaches them. And best of all . . . he gives them presents!"

Jeshua laughed. "Yes. A father gives his children gifts, even life itself. And this world," he said, motioning about, "is a gift from our Heavenly Father."

Arah put the empty urn down and picked up the waterskin, pondering. "So God is our father . . . and we're his children." He tossed the skin into the well. It hit the water with a loud *plop*. The boy hauled the heavy skin up. "I think I know what you mean," he said, pouring the water into the urn, lifting it to Jeshua. "And I'm sorry I didn't offer you this before."

Jeshua cupped his hands and Arah poured the water into them. Jeshua buried his face in the cool, clear water and received another handful, drinking deeply. When he was finished, he straightened and nodded at Arah. "You are just like your father," said Jeshua.

"You knew my father, Philip bar Joakim?" asked the boy, surprised.

Jeshua shook his head. "No. I never met him. Who was he?"

"He was a servant, like me. He died a long time ago. He used to take me into the fields. I would play in the barley while he worked." The boy looked wistful. "He was taller than you are."

"And he was a good father."

"Yes, he was," said Arah thoughtfully. "But if you never met him, why did you say I was just like him?"

Jeshua looked heavenward, and Arah did as well. "Oh," said Arah, smiling. "Like my Heavenly Father."

Jeshua nodded.

"How can that be? How can I be just like him?" asked the boy.

"Good fathers are the same, on earth or in heaven. Your father watched over and cared for you. Heavenly Father watches us as well, and when we need something, he gives it to us."

Arah looked doubtful. "Always?"

"Yes. But sometimes what we think we need is not really what we need. But he knows the difference, and we always receive what is best for us."

Arah looked up at Jeshua, hardness in his eyes. "Then why did he take my father away?"

Jeshua looked at the boy for a long moment, then said, "That's a good question, Arah." He put his hand on the boy's shoulder. "Why don't you ask him?"

Arah looked up. "Ask him? How?"

"Find a place where you can be alone and close your eyes and ask him."

"Will he answer?"

Jeshua smiled. "Yes. But, Arah . . ." The boy looked up at him. "His answers come in many forms. You will have to be patient and listen. Don't be discouraged if the answer doesn't come immediately. Your Heavenly Father will answer you, but remember your own father: he didn't always give you what you wanted the instant you asked for it."

"That's true," said Arah. "When I was little, I asked him if I could work in the fields with him, but he said no, I was too young. I was angry at him."

"Do you think that meant he didn't love you, just because the answer he gave you didn't please you?"

"No," said Arah, shaking his head. "I've worked plenty since then. Maybe it just wasn't time."

"All things have their season, Arah."

"Jeshua, are you a rabbi?"

Jeshua was putting on his leather apron. "No, Arah. I'm a carpenter." He withdrew a worn chisel and examined a nick in the cutting edge.

"So how do you know what you say about Heavenly Father is true?" asked the boy.

"I just do, Arah. And so do you."

Arah looked quizzically at the carpenter, his lips pursed. After a moment of thinking, he nodded. "I guess I do. I just never knew I did."

Jeshua laughed. "So you're getting answers already?"

Arah looked surprised. "Was that an answer? That feeling I just had?"

Jeshua nodded. "Life is funny, isn't it? The answers are there, if we just listen."

Just then Eli stormed out of the house, the door banging hard against a large urn by the entrance, almost knocking it over. He strode past Jeshua and Arah as if they weren't there, stabbing his staff into the ground as he walked, his eyes fixed on the fields beyond the door-yard. He ducked under the grape trellis and continued on across the road toward the green fields, his shoulders hunched and his face red with anger.

Arah looked concerned as he watched Eli pick his way between the rows of low green shoots. He turned back to the well and lowered the waterskin. "But fathers also punish children," he said quietly, his voice echoing in the well. The skin splashed in the water far below. He began raising the rope.

Jeshua looked at Arah, noting his changed mood. "They also forgive."

Arah pulled the skin over the well edge and poured it into the clay urn. He shook his head. "Not all of them."

THREE

SIMEON BAR ELI

By midmorning, Jeshua had unhooked the door from its tired leather hinges and removed the handle and lock. Between trips to the fields with the water jar, Arah kept an eye on him. Something about Jeshua was different. Even though he was busy working, when people said hello, he always stopped and asked them questions—questions that went beyond mere courtesy. Once, when Arah was hauling a load of firewood to the house, he overheard Jeshua's exchange with Hannah, Master Eli's cook, who was drawing water for the kitchen.

"I knew your father," said Hannah, as she tucked a wisp of gray hair back under her scarf. She extended a ladle of water to him. "And your mother. She is well?"

Jeshua drank deeply and handed the ladle back. "Yes. Thank you. And I remember you, Hannah. You lived in Nazareth many years ago. How is your husband, Enan?"

Hannah looked down. "Passed on," she said simply.

"I'm sorry," said Jeshua. "My father always said Enan was a fine man."

Hannah looked up at him, her eyes bright. "He said that? Your father?"

Jeshua nodded.

Hannah straightened and held her head high. "He was a fine man, my Enan." And with that she went back to drawing water, but Arah noticed a smile on her face. Everyone Jeshua talked to was happier after conversing with him, even old Hannah, who was hardly ever happy.

Arah carried the heavy water jar into the fields, filling the large bucket kept there so the workers could have drinking water when they needed it. What Jeshua had said about asking God about his father stayed on his mind. Arah was raised as a practicing Jew; his mother had seen to that. He and his two sisters went to synagogue each Sabbath, and at their yearly Passover seder, two chairs remained empty: his father's and the prophet Elijah's. Arah had come to think of his father as a kind of prophet as well: severe, pious, and serving God in heaven.

But his mother, Muriel, had not taught Arah to pray beyond the short, memorized prayers offered at meals and at bedtime. They had never traveled to Jerusalem for the holy days, not even the Feast of the Tabernacles, because it came during the harvest, and Master Eli would not permit it. They were servants, after all, a shekel or two above slaves. Master Eli was not cruel; he was simply indifferent. Maybe that's why Jeshua had made such an impact on Arah. He'd never had an adult speak to him so directly about anything. He treated Arah like a real person, not just a lowly servant boy. And he listened to him, something no adult had ever done. And what he'd said about talking with God—Heavenly Father—that was something to ponder. When Arah thought about God, he imagined him with Master Eli's stern, bearded face, and so it was hard to imagine God even listening to the prayers of little boys, much less answering them.

Jeshua examined the doorjamb carefully. It was in acceptable condition. A little sanding, filling, and repainting and it might serve a long while yet. He turned to the door, which lay on two sawhorses nearby. He closed his eyes and ran his hands slowly over the old wood to find its weaknesses and strengths, considering by feel how much planing and sanding it would require.

"What are you praying for? More money?"

Jeshua straightened and turned. In the doorway stood a man with dark, curly hair, a little younger than he, dressed in a dirty work tunic, wiping his hands on a rag. Jeshua nodded. "I was praying for the skill to fix this door, sir," he said lightly.

"Don't call me 'sir,' carpenter," said the young man, walking brusquely past him. "I'm a servant here, like her." He pointed at Hannah, who was pouring water into a brown cooking pot sitting on the well surround. He took the pot from her, lifted it to his mouth, and nearly drained it before handing it brusquely back to Hannah, whose eyes were carefully lowered. He ran a sleeve across his mouth and turned to Jeshua.

"Peace be unto you. I'm Jeshua bar Joseph," said Jeshua, bowing his head deferentially.

"From Nazareth. That's a small town."

Jeshua smiled. "Yes. Barely larger than Cana—your nearest town."

The man ignored the rejoinder. "It's hard to find a good carpenter around here."

"That's true. My father is the finest carpenter I know, but he and my brothers are working in Sepphoris, rebuilding after the big fire." He pulled out his hammer and bent over the door.

"Yes," said the young man, watching him with a frown on his face. "That fire has inconvenienced everyone."

Jeshua pulled a bent nail from the door and held it up. "I suppose we'll all have to make do with what we have." He straightened it with two swift blows of his hammer and placed it in his leather apron. "Besides, the more skilled a craftsman is, the more he charges."

"And you're a skilled craftsman, I suppose."

Jeshua shrugged. "My rates are fair."

"Fair to whom?" barked the young man. "Certainly not to me!" Without waiting for an answer, he turned and strode toward the fields.

The skin splashed in the water below, and Jeshua turned. Hannah nodded toward the fields as she pulled the rope up. "That was Simeon, Eli's son."

"Ah," said Jeshua. "His son."

"His elder son," she added.

Jeshua cocked his head at her.

"Master Eli has another son—a younger son— but he has left. Gone into the world."

"I see," said Jeshua. "And Simeon is angry about it."

Hannah nodded and poured the water into the cooking pot. She picked it up and set it on her hip, tossing her green scarf back across her shoulder. She walked toward the house. "Master Simeon is angry about everything."

FOUR

OUT IN THE WORLD

Such a city! Reuben had never seen the like, and he'd been to Jerusalem many times. But while Jerusalem had one glorious structure—the Temple—Damascus had scores of them: the huge, colonnaded porticos of the palace and government buildings, the largest marketplace he'd ever seen, and the incredible, many-storied homes of the wealthy and powerful.

It was a feast for the eyes, which, unfortunately, did not quell the rumblings of his stomach, now empty for most of the day. He'd left home almost a week before, early in the morning, wanting to get away before anyone tried to talk him out of it. Eli pleaded with him to stay, but once Reuben felt the money in his hands, it was as if he was already gone. Nothing anyone could say could make him stay. The only one who hadn't begged him to reconsider was Simeon, who had stood behind his father, arms folded, his mouth set in a straight line, still as a stone.

Reuben might have stayed if Simeon had asked him to. He loved his older brother, even though he had never expressed it. It was quite impossible to tell Simeon anything, much less things of the heart. He was absolutely certain he was right about everything. An admission of love would be seen as proof to Simeon that he was indeed superior to his younger brother. Why, if Reuben ever told his brother how much he respected him, Simeon would hold it over him forever. So Reuben had never said any such thing, and now he was hundreds of miles away, proof that he didn't need anything from Simeon anymore.

This was as it should be. After all, Simeon was the firstborn and by law would receive Eli's entire estate as his inheritance. Reuben felt the money pouch under his tunic, proud of his wisdom in leaving when he did. If he had waited for Eli to die, he would have had to beg his inheritance from Simeon, who would have found an excuse for denying it. And even if Simeon acquiesced and was fair, he would never be generous. He never was, not even with himself. Simeon lived like a miser, and why? He had everything: the love of the beautiful Rachel, the respect of the servants, and the honor of his father. Compared to Simeon, Reuben was a servant. Father had been preparing Simeon to lead from birth, teaching him how to run the estate, when to plant and harvest, how to discipline the workers, and when to indulge them. And Reuben, only three years younger, was left to watch and try to learn by overhearing snippets of their conversations.

Things became very clear to Reuben last year, when Simeon and Rachel got married. Everyone was pleased, but Reuben knew that now that Simeon was married, Eli would soon turn the holdings over to him and Reuben would then have to serve his brother—and there was no way he was going to do that. So he asked his father for his inheritance. He implored, harangued, and begged, and when he threatened to leave without it, Eli finally gave in. He told Reuben his time was coming and he would not be forgotten, and though Reuben wanted to believe him, Simeon's hardness made him doubt.

When Eli withdrew his inheritance from the strongbox, Reuben was amazed at the size of it. A score of large, golden talents—enough to sustain him for the rest of his life—poured out into his hands, and he stood there, looking up into his father's weathered face, astonished, but feeling Simeon's angry eyes on him. Father wasn't smiling, but he wasn't angry, either. He was disappointed, and Reuben understood why. He loved his father and knew his father loved him, but he could not stay. Not to serve a taskmaster like Simeon.

All through the night, Reuben had loaded his train. When he set off at first light, Father stood in the doorway, waving good-bye. Simeon stood behind him, pouting. *He'll be a rich man*, thought Reuben, spurring his camel out of the dooryard, *but he won't rule over me.*

The trip to Damascus had taken a week, and now that he was here, he released the two servants who had accompanied him and bade them farewell. Then he stood in the marketplace in the largest city he'd ever seen and contemplated his future. A man of means in a cultured, exotic city, full of tempting delights to charm the senses. He felt like an ascetic who has spent his life in the wilderness, seeking wisdom among the rocks and sand, but who finally gives up his quest for God and finds his home in Babylon. His long fast was coming to an end. He would indulge himself. He had earned the right. Reuben urged his camel into the busy marketplace. It wasn't long before a man approached him and asked if he could be of service, admiring Reuben's heavily laden caravan.

"You most certainly can," said Reuben expansively, feeling his stomach rumble again. "Do you know where might I get a good meal?"

FIVE

Apprentice

The next morning Jeshua arrived early and stood for fifteen minutes outside the dooryard, waiting to be invited in. Several servants came and went, but no one extended an invitation to enter. Jeshua's donkey was impatient, though, and entered without delay. Jeshua felt peculiar waiting while the donkey headed for the trough. Then a dusty tapestry hung across the doorway was pulled aside and Arah's brown face appeared. His teeth flashed as he yelled, "It's Jeshua! Come in, Jeshua!"

Jeshua walked under the grape trellis. Arah ran to the well and began drawing water. He nodded at the donkey standing at the trough. "It's empty," he said, pulling the waterskin up and running to pour it into the basin. The donkey set to work, slaking its thirst. Arah patted the animal on the haunches. "He's really thirsty," said the boy. He ran back to the well and tossed the skin back down. "I'll get you a drink, too, Jeshua."

Jeshua sat down on the stone well surround. Arah pulled the waterskin up, dipped the ladle in, and handed it to Jeshua, who shook his head. "You first, Arah."

Arah quickly drained the ladle and dipped it again, handing it to Jeshua, who drank the cool water down. Jeshua wiped his mouth and said, "Thanks for the drink." He withdrew something from his cloak and motioned for Arah to extend his hand. "Take this," he said, placing a small nugget of hard candy in Arah's palm.

"For me?" asked Arah, his eyes wide.

Jeshua shook his head. "For him," he said, gesturing at the donkey. Arah was disappointed but walked over and gave the sweet to the donkey anyway. The donkey crunched the candy quickly and went back to drinking. Arah slowly trudged back to the well. Jeshua watched him, smiling at his fallen countenance. "I have something for you, too, Arah," said Jeshua, reaching into his cloak again.

Arah looked up, his eyes bright. "What is it?"

Jeshua withdrew his hand. It held an old metal scraper with a worn wooden handle. He extended the tool to Arah, who took it reluctantly. "What's this?"

"An opportunity."

The boy looked at him suspiciously. "What kind of opportunity?"

"To be my apprentice."

Arah's mouth dropped open. He blinked, twice. "Really?"

Jeshua nodded. "It's just while I'm working for Master Eli. You can learn a lot if—"

"When do I start?" asked Arah, looking at the scraper like it had suddenly changed into gold.

Jeshua said, "First, ask Master Eli for permission. If he approves, and you have time between your other chores, you may help me."

"I'm sure he will!" exulted Arah.

"There is more," said Jeshua, standing. He placed his hands on his hips and regarded the boy evenly.

Arah looked up at him, his eyes bright with hope. "What?"

"As my apprentice, you must watch and listen carefully and do exactly as I say."

"Of course," said Arah, nodding furiously. "I will. Like you were my own father."

Jeshua smiled. "Now you've given *me* a challenge, Arah, asking me to be like your father. I'll do my best not to disappoint you." He reached into his cloak again. "This is for you," he said, withdrawing a sweet and giving it to the boy.

"What's it for?" asked Arah, popping the hard candy into his mouth.

"A reminder," said Jeshua. "Of the gifts our fathers give us."

PLAYING THE PART

"This will do just fine," said Reuben, looking around the large room. "Just fine."

The landlord nodded and pocketed the coins. "If there is anything else you need, please let me know." He left quietly.

Reuben looked out the window at the large house across the square. Two stories of white marble, a flat roof, and green rolling hills beyond. Wide granite steps led up to two huge oak doors. Planters bursting with red and white irises lined the veranda fronting the magnificent, colonnaded building.

"Just like mine," said Reuben proudly. He turned and examined himself in the polished metal reflector he held. A new tunic and cloak of the finest linen, bright blue (not those muted Jewish earth tones), a dashing red leather belt, and a new pair of sandals. His old clothing lay on the floor by the bed, a plush, cush-

ioned affair fit for a king, festooned from the ceiling
with hanging drapes and mosquito netting. He smiled.
He would soon share that bed with a lovely woman,
perhaps the one he met last night at the tavern, the one
with raven hair and flecks of gold on her eyelids. Gold-
en eyelids! Reuben had never imagined such a thing.
After dinner they all went out—Reuben and his new
friends and the beautiful woman—to attend a Greek
theatrical farce with singing and dancing. Imagine!
Singing and dancing, and not at a wedding, either. He
laughed louder than anyone, told the funniest jokes,
and drank more than his share of the sweet plum wine.
And when he saw the woman admiring his expensive
clothes, he knew she would soon be his. After all, he
had to play the part to get the part—a character in the
play had said that. So he intended to perfect the role of
the wealthy young man. Tonight would be a repeat per-
formance of last night; his companions already awaited
him downstairs, drinking wine served by Reuben's new
servants.

He lifted his chin and looked in the mirror. Tonight he would eat the meat of rare game birds, drink
the finest wines of Assyria, marvel at the fascinating
exploits of well-traveled adventurers, and finally, after
midnight, take the golden-eyed woman by the hand
and escort her upstairs, where he would complete his
transformation from country boy to worldly man.

SEVEN

DOOMSAYER

Arah meant to immediately ask Master Eli for permission to help Jeshua, but when Eli strode angrily past him, he was too afraid to speak. After lunch, out in the fields, the men were weeding the rows of barley sprouts. Arah dumped the drinking water into the barrel and walked over to where Micah knelt, pulling weeds.

"Hello, Micah," said Arah, handing him a ladle of water.

"Praise him," said Micah, as he always did, before saying anything else. "I was dying of thirst."

"You'll never die of anything," said Arah, laughing. The old man was always talking about ways he might die, ways other people had died, and what kind of funeral they'd have for him when he was gone—and, on his gloomiest days, what kind of funeral they would *not* have for him when he was gone.

"I'll die," said Micah flatly, looking up at the blazing sun. He was bald but refused to wear a hat. As a result, he was cooked brown like a walnut, and his pale blue eyes and long gray beard made him look like the prophet of doom he was. "I won't be around to harvest this crop, I can tell you that much," he said, frowning.

"You'll eat the bread we make from it," said Arah, smiling. "Even though you don't have any teeth."

"I have teeth," said Micah. "See?" He opened his mouth, and sure enough, there were two teeth on either side of his lower jaw. They were the only two teeth he had, but they were sufficient for gumming barleymeal. "Won't need 'em where I'm going."

"Micah," said Arah. "Can I ask you a question?"

"I might not live long enough to answer it," said Micah morosely.

"Is God really our father?"

Micah squinted up at the boy. "We are his subjects; he is our king. The two are different. Fathers are fallible; they grow old and die. God is infallible and cannot die, so he cannot be our father." Secure in his solid logic, he went back to weeding, moving along the row on his hands and knees, his bony elbows moving rhythmically in his oversized tunic. "Now pitch in or go," he said.

"I have another question," said Arah, following Micah down the row. "The carpenter Jeshua said we could ask God anything and he'd answer us. Is that true?"

"God well knows what we need even before we ask. Our duty is to obey his commandments. If we do, we need not worry for ourselves."

"But does he answer prayers?" pressed Arah.

Micah let out a long sigh. "Obviously not. I'm still here, aren't I?" He turned away, closing the subject.

"Micah?" asked Arah.

"Go away, boy," said Micah.

"Would you ask Master Eli if I could work with the carpenter? He asked me to be his apprentice."

Micah turned around. "You want to leave us?"

"Oh, no," said Arah, shaking his head. "It's just while he's here. I thought I might learn something besides how to fill buckets with water." Micah smiled. It suddenly occurred to Arah that the old man would genuinely miss him if he left. "Master Eli listens to you," said Arah.

Micah laughed. "No one listens to me." He shook his head, his long gray beard ticking back and forth.

"I listen," said Arah quietly.

Micah pointed a finger. "Then listen now: don't believe everything that carpenter says. Sounds like he has some strange ideas."

"But he's nice," said Arah.

"Well, nice or not, mind yourself. Learn what you can about carpentering, but stick to the old ways when it comes to religion. Never steer you wrong. Now, get back to work. I'll square it with Master Eli, if I live long enough to ask him."

Micah didn't die that day, and Arah was given permission to work with Jeshua after his other chores were done. So all afternoon, between trips to the well for the field workers and the women in the house, Arah helped Jeshua, who put him to work scraping the old varnish off the door planks. The boy worked hard to follow Jeshua's instructions. Jeshua complimented him regularly, and they ate their lunch together under the old olive tree shading the well. Arah found a length of twine, threaded it through the hole in the scraper handle, and hung it around his neck, proudly showing it to the other children who played in the dooryard. It was obvious that Arah had achieved a certain status through Jeshua's recognition, and the other children, who had been shy to approach Jeshua before, now came over to watch him work. He took a moment with each one, asking their names and a little about their families.

All day long, Jeshua noticed that Arah's step was livelier as he hurried with his watering chores so he could return to help with the door.

EIGHT

NEWS FROM A DISTANT LAND

A couple of days later, Jeshua finished dismantling the door. It was a long process and required the utmost care and patience. He would gently pour water on the joints and wait for the wood to swell, loosening the glue. Then he would place the door in the hot sun, allowing the timbers to dry and shrink back to their original size. After repeating the process several times, the joints released. The door parts lay in a neat pile near his sawhorses.

Jeshua was examining one of the timbers when someone yelled. He turned and saw Arah running across the green fields toward the house, waving his cloak in the air, shouting, "Master Eli! Master Eli!"

Within moments, Eli emerged from the house, pulling on his cloak.

Arah leaped over the low rock fence and ground to a stop before Eli, panting. "It's Azariah! Returning from Damascus!"

The old man stared at Arah, then leaned heavily against the door frame, his hand on his forehead, muttering, "Damascus?"

Arah nodded, trying to catch his breath.

Jeshua looked at the road. Clearing a stand of junipers at the edge of the property, a caravan of mules and camels appeared, loaded down with a merchant's wares.

"My staff," shouted Eli. Arah ducked inside and reappeared with the old man's walking staff. Eli took it and draped his other arm over Arah's shoulders, and together they walked slowly toward the advancing caravan. Jeshua noted Eli's eyes were bright as he passed. By the time he had reached the wooden gate at the low stone wall, the caravan had arrived.

A small, well-fed man jumped down from his camel and walked briskly toward Eli. They met in the gateway and hugged each other fiercely, kissing each other on the cheeks. The rotund merchant pulled away and looked up at Eli. "Peace be unto you, Eli, my old friend!"

"And unto you, peace, Azariah," said Eli "You have news? Of Reuben?"

Azariah frowned. "Slake my thirst and I will tell you all I know."

Eli motioned at Arah, who came running with the waterskin. "One must always bargain with you, Azariah," he said heartily.

Azariah took the ladle and drained it. Then he took another and did likewise. His entourage was large, with ten camels and a dozen horses and mules. They looked tired. He waved the riders down and pointed to the well, raising his eyebrows at Eli.

"Of course!" said Eli, waving them in. "Come in. Water your stock. Azariah, come inside, I want to hear everything!"

They advanced a few paces into the dooryard when Azariah stopped, his face serious. He looked up at Eli. "It's been a hard journey, and a long one."

"Yes, I'm sure," said Eli, motioning for him to continue inside.

Azariah stood his ground. "As fits such a journey, I have hard news, Eli."

The old man seemed to sag. He bent his head toward Azariah. "Of Reuben?"

Azariah nodded. And waited.

"Please," said Eli quietly.

"Reuben is yet alive—thanks to the Master of the Universe. But he is not well."

"My boy is sick?" asked Eli, shocked. "What sickness?"

"Sickness of the soul, Eli. He is living riotously, drunk much of the time, consorting with harlots," said Azariah, barely above a whisper. And . . ." he paused and lowered his eyes, "blaspheming the Lord. God forgive him."

Eli's hand went to the neck of his tunic, pulling it down, straining the fabric. His eyes were wild. He ran a hand through his shaggy gray hair in dismay. "You've seen him?" he finally asked, as if from a great distance, his voice small and thin.

"I've seen him," affirmed Azariah.

Eli shook his head in disbelief. "So he *is* in Damascus, as I had guessed. Among the Assyrians?"

Azariah nodded his head sadly. "I asked him if he had a message for you."

"And what did he say?"

Azariah shook his head. "He laughed at me." Azariah put his hand on Eli's shoulder. "I'm sorry, Eli."

Eli shook his hand off and straightened, his eyes looking heavenward. He grabbed at the neck of his tunic with both hands and split his shirt to his belt. Nearby servants took a step backward, familiar with Eli's rare but terrible fury.

"What will you do?" asked Azariah carefully.

Eli turned, his head bowed with grief. Azariah made to follow him, but Eli waved him away. "There is nothing I can do. He has chosen his path," he said as he trudged toward the house. As he passed Jeshua, Eli said to himself, "God's punishment must fall."

After Eli disappeared indoors, all eyes turned to Azariah, still standing by the well. He looked heavenward. "Forgive me, Lord, for bearing these bad tidings. Send your angels to lighten Eli's heart."

From inside, Jeshua heard Eli's voice. He could not make out what he was saying, but he was in heated conversation with someone. Azariah's company came into the dooryard to water their stock, but Eli's servants stood frozen, not knowing what to do. They looked apprehensively at the house, as if it might say something. The talking inside continued, voices raised.

Then, after several minutes, Simeon appeared in the doorway, shaking his head. He said, to no one in particular, "I knew it," and walked into the dooryard. Seeing Azariah, his eyes lit up, but there was still darkness in him. "Azariah!" he shouted, slapping the little merchant on the back and steering him toward the camels. "What have you brought us?"

Jeshua turned back to his work. He steadied a door plank across a sawhorse, adjusted his plane's cutting edge, and worked steadily, planing in long, even strokes. Shortly, he heard a noise behind him. There was Eli in the doorway, his features a thundercloud of anger. At his appearance, the servants sprang into action and went about their business. Eli squinted at the crowd at the well, then turned his gaze toward Azariah's camel beyond the wall, which was being unloaded. A rug had been thrown over the low stone wall, and wares were being arranged upon it. Examining the merchandise, Simeon stood, his arms folded and his brow furrowed. To his side stood Azariah, who kept glancing over his shoulder at Eli. Simeon looked at Eli, then fixed his interest on the goods.

Jeshua turned toward Eli. "Master Eli?" Eli's torn shirt revealed his gray chest hair, wet with tears.

"Master Eli, I have a question."

Eli frowned at Jeshua. "It's none of your business, carpenter."

Jeshua nodded. "It's about the door. There's a problem."

Eli smiled bitterly. "There always is," he said.

Jeshua gestured at the plank he'd been planing. "See this?" A rough brown oval lay inside the smooth, newly planed section. "Wood rot. And here," he said, picking up a torn leather hinge. "The hinges are beyond repair. And finally," he said as he picked up the diagonal cross member, "This: it's so warped I cannot plane it straight without destroying its strength."

Eli glanced at the door but then looked back at Simeon and Azariah. He waved Jeshua away. "It looks fine to me, carpenter. Just fix it as best you can."

Jeshua moved into Eli's field of vision, between the old man and Simeon beyond the wall. "It cannot be fixed, sir," he said quietly. "It's too old and worn out."

"Nonsense. You haven't the experience to—"

Jeshua snapped the cross member over his knee and dropped the two pieces on the ground with a clatter. Eli, his attention now fully Jeshua's, raised his chin, but the hardness quickly went out of his eyes. "What do you propose?" he asked, his voice flat.

Jeshua walked toward the doorway. Eli followed him. Jeshua turned and said, "A new door, Master Eli, but made of the finest wood. Mahogany, I believe, would serve best. It will be thicker and stronger than the old oak door, yet lighter and easier to open."

Eli looked over at Simeon and Azariah. Simeon stood with his arms folded, nodding at Azariah. Even from this distance, Jeshua could see the haughtiness in Simeon's stance. Eli turned back to Jeshua, then looked at the broken cross member on the ground.

"All right, carpenter. A new door. Just be quick about it."

And with that he turned and walked inside.

NINE

A Righteous Man

Three days later, Jeshua arrived with a load of new wood on the back of his donkey. He was unloading it, thinking about the drawing of the door he had sketched the night before on a piece of parchment. It was a simple design, and though he was no architect, he thought it would serve nicely. He felt the folded plan in his pocket as he pulled the timber off the donkey, eager to discuss it with Eli, who needed something to take his mind off his two disappointing sons. Jeshua was giving the donkey a handful of grain when someone said, "Ho, now, what's this?"

He turned and saw Simeon standing next to the pile of new timber. He was pointing at the wood but looking at Jeshua. Jeshua walked over to Simeon. "Peace be unto you, Master Simeon. Is Master Eli around this morning?" he asked.

"He's gone to Cana. And I asked you a question, carpenter."

"It's wood for the new door, mahogany—"

"New door?" barked Simeon. "What new door?"

Jeshua nodded toward the door frame, now draped by the tapestry. "The old door was beyond repair," he said.

Simeon laughed sharply and shook his head. "Carpenter, are you a righteous man?"

Jeshua was taken aback. "The Lord will decide if I am."

Simeon laughed bitterly. "Well, you must be, because your prayers have been answered: you've managed to wheedle even more money out of my father."

Jeshua crossed his arms across his chest and looked evenly at Simeon.

"Isn't that right?" taunted Simeon.

Jeshua said quietly, "Simeon, what have I done to anger you?"

Simeon turned on his heel. "You are here, carpenter. And by the time you and others like you are gone, there will be nothing left to inherit."

Jeshua watched him march across the dooryard and jump the low stone wall, heading for the fields.

TEN

LIFE OF THE PARTY

"Do you ever think about your home?" asked Rahab, sipping her wine.

"Yes, Reuben," said Ahmad. "Won't you tell us about Galilee?"

Reuben shook his head. "The answer to both questions is *no*."

There was a great shout as the people around the table leaned forward, eager to hear what Reuben refused to say. But he was drunk and afraid he'd say something to reveal his low origins. He'd learned the hard way, weeks before when he had arrived in Damascus, to be careful of his tongue. "You learn by listening," old Eli had always said, and in this case he was right. There was nothing he wanted to tell them about Galilee, but much *he* wanted to know about it. When Azariah approached him in the tavern two weeks ago, he wanted to ask his old friend how Eli and Simeon were doing, but he was too drunk then as well. Azariah stood there while Reuben's new friends ridiculed his clothing, speech, and weight—all in good fun, of course. But Azariah was not amused, and the hurt on his face shamed Reuben. All through Reuben's youth Azariah had brought him a gift every time the caravan passed Eli's estate: a large, pink shell from the Middle Sea, a rough stone from the Temple mount, colorful glass beads from Greece. He had always been kind to Reuben, yet there he stood, suffering the insults, while Reuben's tongue proved too thick with wine to defend him. And when Azariah finally asked if he had a message for his father, Reuben had laughed, mostly out of embarrassment. Azariah bent his head and left. The rowdy crowd cheered, but Reuben felt sand filling his heart. He drank so much that night he couldn't remember how he got home.

Rahab leaned in, her perfume making Reuben's head spin even more than the wine. She batted her golden eyelids. "Tell *me* about Galilee, then. I can keep a secret."

"That's true, Reuben," said Ahmad. "She kept her true vocation a secret from you for almost two weeks!" Everyone laughed. Reuben blushed. It was true. He thought Rahab was just a beautiful woman who was interested in him. And while she was beautiful, she was never interested in him, only in his money. By now she had managed to get hold of quite a bit of it. Reuben had no doubt that her questions about Galilee were just another way to find out if he had more money there.

"Come, Reuben," said Rahab. "We have better things to do."

Everyone laughed as she tugged on Reuben's arm. But tonight he would not give in. Many nights she had taken him back to his house, and the next morning, when he woke up alone, he noticed things were different: vases shifted, clothing in drawers rumpled, doors open that were closed the night before. Things missing. And yet, the next day, when he went out and stopped by her house, Rahab would be there, smiling prettily at him as always. She would take his hand and walk with him through the marketplace to buy clothing or jewelry or hand mirrors—with Reuben's money, of course.

Reuben looked around at the gathering. His entourage had grown to more than twenty people—some of whose names he didn't even know—and their nightly *bacchanalias* were becoming more of an event than the theaters and taverns and inns they frequented. Reuben noticed how people whispered when they passed, shaking their heads, some frowning, but all willing to take the gold coins he offered. Yes, they might think he and his friends were ill behaved, drunken, and loud, but they lined up to be paid for what little they did to earn the money he gave them.

"I have to talk to Ahmad," said Reuben, shaking Rahab's hand off his arm and standing unsteadily. He pointed at the tall, sandy-haired man sitting across from them. Out of the corner of his eye he saw Rahab scowl and turned to face her, but she was smiling sweetly at him again. "I'll be back," he said, furrowing his brow at her, daring her to disagree.

"I'll be here," she said, winking.

Reuben motioned Ahmad aside. They stood near the door of the crowded tavern. "I am concerned about the investment," said Reuben, taking care that his words did not slur.

Ahmad placed his hand on Reuben's shoulder. "It is going fine, don't worry."

"I *am* worried," emphasized Reuben. "It's been too long. You said the merchandise would be here a week ago."

Ahmad shrugged. "It's here when it's here. Patience, Reuben."

Reuben shook Ahmad's hand from his shoulder. "I've been patient enough. I want results."

Ahmad looked Reuben square in the eye. "Reuben," he said quietly, bending toward the shorter man, "it will be here. Don't pester me any more about this."

He turned and walked back toward the crowd at the tables. Reuben watched him walk away, scowling.

"Sir?" came a voice.

Reuben turned. "What is it?"

The innkeeper, a short, thin man with wisps of brown hair plastered across his bald head, stood before him. "If you please."

Reuben waved him away. "I'll settle with you when we leave."

"Perhaps you forget," said the small man uncomfortably. "You left last night without paying."

Reuben frowned at him. "That's not true. I always pay my bills."

"I'm sure that's true. But you were rather . . . uh . . . *inebriated* when you left. Perhaps you forgot."

Reuben shook his head. "I'm never so drunk that I forget whose hand is in my pocket, innkeeper," he hissed. "You're lying."

The man's face went bright red. "Please, sir, I beg of you. I am not lying. I am simply telling you you're behind in your account. It's the truth."

"Reuben!" called Rahab. "Come back. Nidab has a story about Babylon you must hear!"

Reuben turned back to the innkeeper. "I don't have the money now."

"What?"

"I don't carry that kind of money on me," whispered Reuben. "What kind of fool do you think I am?"

The innkeeper frowned at Reuben. "Perhaps you are the kind of fool who doesn't carry enough money to pay his bills." His eyes bored into Reuben's.

"I'll pay you when I pay you," snapped Reuben, echoing Ahmad. "Tomorrow."

"Sir, I must object—"

"I said tomorrow. Now I'm done with you. Send someone to my house in the morning. And don't mention this in front of my friends."

"Your friends," said the innkeeper sarcastically, "could help you pay your bill."

"My friends are my business," said Reuben.

"Your business, it appears, is spending money you don't have. I will send a boy around tomorrow, before your business suffers any more . . . losses." He turned on his heel and walked away, humble no more.

Reuben glared at him. "Reuben! Come back!" pleaded Rahab, patting the pillow next to her.

"Yes, Reuben, come back," shouted Ahmad. "We're thirsty!"

Everyone laughed.

POINTED QUESTIONS

Eli dismounted slowly from his black horse and shook the dust from his cloak. He glanced around the deserted street and sighed. Looking up, he saw the upper window where Benjamin worked. A sheer curtain shifted in the morning breeze, and for some reason Eli was not surprised at all when he saw Benjamin's white-whiskered face suddenly appear in the window.

"Eli, my friend, what brings you to Cana?" asked Benjamin, leaning out of the window.

Eli looked around, glad the street was empty. "Peace be unto you, Rabbi. I need your counsel."

Benjamin shook his head. "And unto you, peace. No, Eli, it is *your* counsel that is needed. Come up."

Eli made his way up the narrow outside stairs cut into the stone wall. The door at the top opened and Benjamin appeared. He was a tall man, taller even than

Eli, but his shoulders were narrow and he walked bent forward, his large hands hanging from his thin arms like oversized gloves.

Benjamin's tailor shop was, as usual, a complete disaster. Mounds of material lay about; a dozen half-completed tunics and robes hung on hooks by the door. Another tailor hunched over his work, his eyes mere inches from the fabric as he meticulously sewed stitch after stitch.

Benjamin motioned Eli in and returned to his own stool by the window, which was surrounded by waist-high piles of colorful material. Eli looked around. There was no place to sit, so he stood uncomfortably in the center of the room.

Benjamin picked up a striped fabric of at least ten radiant colors, a veritable rainbow. "Like Joseph's coat, no, Eli? Colors and colors and more colors. I bought it on a whim because of its beauty. So, now that you're here, tell me: what shall I make of it?"

Eli shrugged, shifting his weight to his other leg.

Benjamin reached up into his head covering and withdrew a needle, deftly threading it, all the while looking at Eli, a question on his face but none on his lips. Again, Eli shifted his weight and looked over at the other tailor, who was busy sewing.

Finally, Benjamin said loudly, "Goodness, Daniel, leave us in peace. Eli is here to talk to me. Alone."

Daniel raised his head and squinted at Eli. "Oh, Eli, I didn't hear you come in. My apologies." He stood and quickly exited the room.

Eli reached for Daniel's stool and pulled it over toward Benjamin. Now only the large mounds of fabric separated them.

"Daniel," sighed Benjamin, shaking his head. "Deaf and blind, but what hands! He can thread a needle behind his back, under water, in the dark." He laughed, but when he saw Eli sitting there so stiffly on the small stool, he raised his chin toward the old man. "Eli, my friend."

"Rabbi," said Eli, and his voice trailed off. He looked at his sandals and laced his fingers together, shaking his head. "I . . . I . . . don't know how to—"

"Reuben," said Benjamin quietly.

Eli looked up, surprised.

"The trade route passes Cana before it reaches your home."

Eli's face drained of color. "Then you know."

Benjamin took a stitch and looked out the window.

Eli buried his head in his hands and shook it slowly. "So everyone knows."

Benjamin looked at Eli, who finally raised his head to meet his gaze. "Yes, including the Lord."

"That is what I wanted to talk to you about, Rabbi. You know what Reuben has done." Benjamin nodded gravely. Eli continued, "He has broken the commandments and violated the Law. And I know the Lord's justice must fall upon him."

Benjamin put his work aside and leaned forward, pointing his needle at Eli. "But you are wondering about your justice—what *you* should do."

Eli nodded miserably.

Benjamin looked past Eli and quoted scripture, "'The wicked shall be cut off from the earth, and the transgressors shall be rooted out of it.'"

Eli groaned.

Benjamin continued, "'To do justice and judgment is more acceptable to the Lord than sacrifice.'"

Eli shook his head. "Does it really say that?"

Benjamin continued, "You know the Law as well as I do, Eli. And you know it must be obeyed: the sinner shall be punished."

Eli nodded again, looking at the floor.

"It has always been that way," said Benjamin quietly. "From the beginning of time. Justice must prevail. The wicked must be punished so the name of the Lord will be glorified."

"But . . . he's my son," said Eli simply, his eyes pleading with Benjamin.

Benjamin sighed. "Eli, my friend. Every wicked man is someone's son. But that cannot shield them from the Lord's justice."

"But what about mercy?" pleaded Eli. "Has mercy no place?"

Again Benjamin focused on the wall behind Eli. "When the Lord gave the Law to Moses, he said he would show mercy unto those who kept his commandments. Only those who kept his commandments. All others must suffer the sword of his justice."

Eli shook his head but said nothing for a long time. Even Benjamin seemed out of words. He scanned the piles of colorful fabric, searching his mind for consolation for his friend, a man he loved with all his heart and a man who deserved better than he was getting, both from his son and from his rabbi. A particular pattern of colors caught his eye. They formed a rainbow, and Benjamin remembered another of the Lord's promises. "But there is hope," he said slowly.

Eli looked up and nodded at Benjamin to continue.

Benjamin took a deep breath and leaned forward. "The prophet Isaiah foretold of the day when the Messiah would come. All things will change, like winter changes to spring. Our enemies will be vanquished, and the Messiah will teach us a new law, some say a higher law."

"What is this higher law?" asked Eli.

"I do not know. I only know that on that day the Messiah will come and save his people."

"Even my Reuben?" asked Eli.

Benjamin picked up the fabric and carefully made a stitch. He shrugged. "As I said, I do not know. But when the Messiah comes, the Law of Moses will be fulfilled. Everything will change." He looked heavenward and closed his eyes. "May the Messiah come quickly."

Eli nodded and closed his eyes as well, a prayer on his lips. "Yes. May the Messiah come quickly."

TWELVE

AN OBEDIENT SON

E li returned home after dark. Jeshua had been hoping to see him all day to show him the door design, but when Eli came into the dooryard, he waved Jeshua off and walked inside, tired from his trip. Jeshua busied himself working on the doorjamb, sanding smooth the wood insert patches he had fashioned. Inside, Eli's feet were being washed by a servant girl. Simeon stood by, impatient at the slowness of the ritual. When she finally finished, Simeon sat on a large cushion opposite his father.

From the doorway Jeshua saw that Eli took some time to notice Simeon, instead studying a census tally of his flocks. Jeshua felt the tension in the air and wished he were somewhere else. But until Eli approved the door design, he had to work on the jamb; there was nothing else to do.

Finally, Eli looked at Simeon and said, "You may speak."

Simeon leaned forward. "Thank you, Father. I have something to say about Reuben, if I may."

"You may not," said Eli with finality.

Simeon shook his head slowly, anger building in his dark eyes, and moved to get up. When he was at the doorway, Eli spoke. "You've always been an obedient son, Simeon."

Simeon turned back. His father sat amid the cushions, his dinner on a tray next to him, uneaten. Eli looked very old tonight, and Simeon felt bad for him. "I've always tried to be," he said quietly, returning to his cushion and seating himself. He waited, looking at Eli, who was lost in thought.

"You are my firstborn," said Eli.

Jeshua sanded the doorjamb. He wished his sanding stone were silent, but neither Eli nor Simeon seemed to notice him working just a few paces away.

"You have been faithful and obedient to me."

Simeon nodded. "I will always be obedient to you, Father."

Eli took a deep breath. "I know. Speak your heart, then, Simeon. Even if it is hard, I will hear you."

Simeon once again leaned forward. "Reuben has been gone for some time," he began slowly. "The reports we've received reveal his disrespect for the Lord."

"The Lord loves your brother, Simeon, as do I. And whom the Lord loves, he chastens."

Simeon laughed. "Chastens? Azariah says Reuben is drunk all the time, spending money on expensive clothing, gambling, and consorting with harlots and blasphemers!" The last word came out like a curse. He looked away and just managed to catch Jeshua's eye. He frowned at the carpenter, then turned back to Eli, nodding toward Jeshua.

Eli ignored the hint. "What is it, Simeon? Can you not see the pain this causes me?"

"I'm sorry, but I don't see any chastening, by the Lord or by anyone else. But let's suppose the Lord does punish Reuben. Then whatever he suffers is God's justice. Certainly you must see that. He takes his inheritance before his rightful time, squanders it, and dirties our family name in a distant land. The roads are full of talk of his wickedness, and we are laughed to scorn!" He sat back, his chest heaving with righteous indignation.

Eli's head was bowed. After a long time, he asked slowly, "What do you want, Simeon?"

Simeon gritted his teeth. "Cut him off, Father. Let everyone know he is no longer your son—as he is no longer my brother, and—"

"Enough!" yelled Eli, the rafters shaking with his anger. "Enough, I tell you!" He looked at Simeon with slit eyes, full of fire. "You tell me things I already know! I know the commandments better than you! I know the Lord's punishment will fall upon Reuben; must mine fall also?"

"He has disrespected you, Father," said Simeon flatly.

"Yes. He has," said Eli, his eyes smoldering still.

"The Law and the prophets are clear: he must be cut off. You know this is true."

Eli groaned, so loud and so sad that Jeshua had to leave. He stood outside in the darkness, the rectangle of yellow light spilling across the stoop behind him. His heart ached for Eli, but it ached even more for Simeon's bitterness. From inside, he heard nothing, just Simeon's breathing. After a moment, footsteps passed across the flagstones. A door closed.

For a long time Jeshua stood, looking west. A tiny sliver of purple lined the rolling horizon, the remnant of a colorful sunset. He listened for movement inside but heard nothing. Perhaps Eli had left the room as well. He felt the parchment in his apron. He went to the doorway and looked in.

Eli sat, staring into the distance, alone in the room. Jeshua gingerly knocked on the door frame. Eli's great head slowly turned toward him, his gray eyes glazed and red. Jeshua noted that the tears the old man had been shedding hung to the gray strands of his beard. He seemed entirely gray, his clothing, his hair, his beard. Even his skin seemed gray. "What is it, carpenter?" the old man asked weakly.

Jeshua stepped inside. "I'm sorry, Master Eli, but I need you to look over the design for the new door."

"Will it ever be done?" asked Eli wearily.

"Building a door takes time, but yes, it will soon be done."

Eli waved Jeshua over and took the parchment. He examined it for a long time, tracing the lines with his finger but saying nothing. He handed the parchment back. "Fine, carpenter. Now, go . . . I care not for doors or anything else. I have lost a son."

Jeshua walked toward the doorway, then stopped. He turned slowly to see the old man sobbing quietly into his robe. Jeshua said, "Master Eli, one more thing."

The old man continued crying.

"The new door. It should open inward." He waited.

Eli looked up and wiped his eyes. "Inward? Doors don't open inward, carpenter. An apprentice knows that."

"I know," said Jeshua, nodding. "They never have, for many reasons: protection—a door that opens out cannot be battered in—simplicity, tradition, and so on. But this door, this fine, beautiful mahogany door we are building, should open inward, to welcome travelers, friends, and family. A door that opens inward invites all to share the love and bounty of the household."

Eli shook his head and laughed bitterly. He mouthed the words love and bounty, but no sound escaped his lips. He blinked at Jeshua. "While all else in my life lies in ruins around me, here you are, talking to me about a door. A door. As if it mattered." He shook his head again. "I was about to terminate this project, but you have piqued my curiosity and I long to think about something besides my two disappointing sons. A door that opens inward. That I must see."

Jeshua folded the parchment and placed it in his tunic, bowed, and walked outside. As he led his donkey homeward along the silver path in the cool darkness, he looked up at the bright band of stars crossing the black sky and thought of his own father.

THIRTEEN

MICAH'S PREDICTION

For several days Jeshua worked steadily on the new door. The days were hot and there was no shade, except for the large olive tree that guarded the well. Jeshua thought of setting his work up under the old tree but reconsidered. The sawdust he was raising might sift down and dirty the well water. Instead, he settled for the shade offered by the house in the morning; by afternoon he worked in the full, hot sun.

The mahogany he'd purchased for the door was from Antioch. It was expensive, and he had haggled long and hard with the timber merchant, but in the end both of them got a bargain. The wood was aromatic as he sawed it, a sweet, dark smell that pleased him. From the time he was a boy, he had always loved the smell of newly cut wood and hated to varnish over it. But wood soon darkened and rotted without protective coating, so Jeshua enjoyed the brisk, lively odor while he could. In the evenings, after a long day at work, when he bathed before prayers and dinner, he often regretted washing away that sweet smell, even as the water sluiced off the dirt and grime. Often, when he toweled dry after his bath, he would consider how lucky he was to enjoy the pungent smell of worked wood, even though he was getting dirty in the process. But refreshed from his bath, dressed in clean clothes, his hair oiled and combed, he would bend his head over the evening meal and thank God for the privilege of working at something he loved, even as his muscles ached from a long day's labor. Later, in the stillness of night, sleep came swiftly to the carpenter, a deep, untroubled sleep he knew he would not always enjoy.

One day at lunch, Jeshua sat with the servants under the olive tree, enjoying a story Hannah was telling about a young calf that several of the small children had been trying in vain to catch. The calf bawled loudly, she said, enclosed in a ring of children, who were covered with mud from scrambling after it, yet the calf's smooth tan coat remained perfectly clean, untouched by any of them.

"Did they catch it?" asked Arah, caught up in the story.

Hannah picked up a skewer resting over the fire. She pulled off a piece of meat and popped it into her mouth. "What do you think?" she asked, grinning broadly.

Arah was shocked. "We're eating it—right now?" He looked at Hannah in dismay.

Hannah laughed and shook her head. "No . . . but we will!" She winked at the boy.

Everyone laughed as she pointed to the small stock pen near the side of the house. There, the same small brown calf stood, looking curiously at them as if it knew they were talking about it.

Micah didn't laugh but shook his head. "We won't be eating that calf. Ever."

"Why not?" asked a servant. "It's fat. It would make a tasty meal."

"That it would," added Hannah, still chewing the piece of meat.

Micah stood, finished with his lunch. "Master Eli is saving that calf for young Reuben's return." He shook his head and slowly walked from the circle.

Everyone sat in silence for a moment, then Hannah nodded and said, "I'm afraid Micah is right. That calf will outlive us all."

FOURTEEN

A Distant Star

For several days Arah considered Micah's words of warning about the carpenter. He'd known Micah all his life. He knew the old man to be kind, if a bit gloomy. He'd known Jeshua only a few days but already felt Jeshua loved him like a son. He wanted to believe what the carpenter said. Jeshua had stated that "The truth always tastes good, if we're hungry for it." Arah was hungry for answers, and the things Jeshua said about God and answers to prayers not only tasted good, they echoed in his soul, making him think about life in new ways.

Until Jeshua arrived, Arah felt that he'd spent his whole life looking at the ground, lugging heavy water buckets to and from the fields, or staring into the blackness of the well, hauling the wet, slimy rope up, to empty the waterskin and drop it again. Repetition was the nature of his life, day in and day out, and he

was just a boy. He wondered if he would still be hauling water when he was as old as Micah, who crawled
along the rows of barley, his eyes also focused on the
ground.

But something about Jeshua made him look up
at the heavens with new eyes. He began to see faces in
the fluffy white clouds, feel the miracle of the sun on
his face, and imagine his father walking the streets of
heaven with God. The thought made Arah's eyes mist,
and he had to turn away so Jeshua wouldn't see him.
But the image tasted so good that he wanted to hug
Jeshua and thank him for taking away the image of his
father dying on his low, hard bed, eyes sunken, skin
yellow, and his hair falling out. "Consumption," they
called it; Mother said it was the "wasting disease," and
when Father died, he weighed no more than Arah.

And yet Jeshua talked about Arah's father as if he
was still alive and well. He said Philip was still Arah's
father and remained concerned about him. What kind
of boy would he grow up to be? Would he be honest?
Kind? Generous? Or would he be angry, sullen, and
bitter, like so many people? Jeshua said everyone's life
was hard—he showed Arah a number of white, ridged
scars on his own hands—but a hard life didn't have to
make us hard as well.

And when Arah protested, saying he was a water boy and that would never change, Jeshua handed him his hammer and asked, "Are you a carpenter yet?"

"No," said Arah, hefting the heavy hammer.

"So you're still a water boy?"

Arah nodded. "That's what I mean."

Jeshua held out a piece of wood and handed Arah a small nail. "Hammer it in."

Arah did so. The nail, miraculously, went straight in. He looked up and smiled.

"Now you're a carpenter, Arah," said Jeshua. "Things are changing already."

Arah was standing in Eli's orchard now, hidden among the fig trees. It was well after dinner, and he'd sneaked out, his head full of conflict and heart full of hope. He had queried Jeshua all day, as subtly as he could, about the mechanics of prayer and how answers came. Jeshua told him little, except to say that faith was important.

Arah knelt, wondering if he had faith. Jeshua said faith was believing in something that was true, even though you couldn't see it. Arah knew his father existed once, but he wasn't sure if he still did. If it was true, and he believed it, then he supposed he had this faith Jeshua was talking about. But the belief felt like a small smooth stone in his hand—comforting and warm, but of no real use.

He sat down on a rock and looked up at the sky between the trees. The stars twinkled in the darkness. Jeshua said they were suns, like our sun. Micah had laughed when Arah told him that, shaking his head. "Foolishness," he'd said. "They're not suns. Look how small they are," and he'd gone back to his weeding.

"But they're far away, that's what Jeshua says," the boy had countered.

Micah had pointed a gnarled finger at the boy. "Watch yourself, Arah," he'd said.

Arah, like all boys, knew about the wheel of the night sky, how it spun around the north star. He imagined God and his own father living on that star, or else why would everything revolve around it? So he focused on the star, perched above the horizon, and closed his eyes.

"Heavenly Father," he said, trying to picture God, but only Micah's grizzled face came into his mind's eye. He shook his head and tried again, but this time Jeshua's face came into focus. He had white hair and a long white beard, but it was still Jeshua, and Arah wondered at the image, which persisted, so he went on: "Jeshua says my father is with you. Is it true?"

He listened to the wind sighing through the trees and the crickets chirping. The night was warm, but he shivered, knees pulled up, arms around them. Nothing came.

He opened his eyes and looked at the star. "Why did you take him away?" The star twinkled distantly, and Arah was distracted by movement in the orchard. He turned. A dog, maybe, or a squirrel. He turned back to the star. "Why?" he asked, his lips barely moving, holding his breath.

He sat there for a long time, listening. But no voice whispered. No inner voice, either, the kind Jeshua had said to listen for. The star twinkled but said nothing. Finally, he gave up.

As he walked back to the family quarters, he wondered how long he'd been out there. The oil lamp still burned inside. The moon had not yet risen. *There is more to being a carpenter than swinging a hammer,* he thought. *And there is more to prayer than asking and listening.*

FIFTEEN

RACHEL AND SIMEON

Simeon hated the fields. The work was dirty, and the sun beat down on his back like a slaver's lash. He straightened from weeding the seedlings and put his hands on the small of his back, grimacing. He looked around. The other laborers were congregated together, laughing as they worked, enjoying a private joke. He noted that they never worked near him. They worked hard enough; the rows were weeded and watered, but they made him feel like an outsider, even though he was their master.

Of course they're happy, he thought, gathering up a bunch of weeds and tossing them into a large woven basket. *They have no hope of anything more. They've come to accept their lot. But I cannot.*

He straightened again and looked around for the servant boy. He was nowhere in sight. "Where's that boy?" he called out to no one in particular.

"He's helping the carpenter, Master Simeon," said old Micah, whose back was too stiff to bend over anymore. Instead, he worked the rows on his hands and knees. It embarrassed Simeon to see Micah working this way, but when he'd suggested the old man help the women around the house, Micah had shaken his head furiously. "I will work like a man until I die," he'd said with finality. But watching him work on his hands and knees made Simeon uncomfortable, and he tried whenever he could to give Micah work that was less strenuous. Micah did as he was told, but it soon became clear to Simeon that he preferred working with the other men, so Simeon threw up his hands and let things be. It seemed he had no impact at all on the servants. He was just another worker, and though they called him "master," he knew they had no love for him. They respected him, perhaps because he was the hardest worker of all, starting in the fields at the break of day and continuing until nightfall. Yet no one ever complimented him or expressed gratitude for the work he did. It was simply expected of him.

Simeon grabbed a bunch of weeds and pulled them from the ground. Sweat ran into his eyes. He could feel it trickling down his spine. And he was thirsty. Where was that boy?

Oh, yes, helping the carpenter. The carpenter who had managed to turn a two-day job into a three-week stay. And the way the children flocked around him, listening to him and running errands for him, galled Simeon. Why did this carpenter deserve all the attention? Would he be here in a month, laboring with the servants in the hot sun, worrying about their families and what would happen to them if the harvest was poor or nonexistent? No, he would be gone, off to another job, caring nothing about these people. And yet they would speak glowingly of him, even within earshot of Simeon, not understanding that Simeon cared more deeply for all of them, and without pay or gratitude, than this carpenter ever would.

His anger was making him even thirstier. "Where is that boy?" he yelled loudly, even as he pulled another clump of grass.

"Simeon, don't shout," said a gentle voice.

Simeon looked up. It was Rachel. She stood behind him, a water urn on her hip, holding an overflowing ladle out toward him, smiling.

"Rachel!" he said, jumping up, taking the ladle and draining it. "How did you know I was thirsty?"

Rachel laughed, a clear, sparkling laugh that made Simeon forget his anger. "A man craves water as a woman craves a kind word." She dipped the ladle into the urn and gave it to him again.

Simeon drank it, the water running down his beard and onto his tunic. He ran a brown hand across his mouth and smiled. "You've satisfied my thirst, so now I will satisfy yours. You are more beautiful every day."

Rachel motioned old Micah over. He came as quickly as his old bones would allow and took the water urn to the other workers. She turned back to Simeon. "Thank you, husband," she said, her green eyes bright with pleasure. She put both hands on her large stomach. "We both thank you."

Simeon smiled. "How do you—both of you—feel today?"

"I am tired and he is restless." She patted her stomach. "We keep different hours. I fear he will outrun you when he is a year old."

Simeon nodded. "I can't wait for that race."

Rachel grew serious. "I cannot wait, either, Simeon. We cannot wait. Have you spoken to your father?"

Simeon put his arm around Rachel and led her a few steps away, out of earshot of the others. He whispered, "I've pled with him a number of times that our time has come."

"But he is not persuaded," said Rachel flatly.

"No," answered Simeon, his eyes downcast. "He is not persuaded."

"Then you must no longer plead—you must demand," she said.

Simeon looked at his lovely wife. Her dark, wavy hair was gathered at the neck, framing her flawless skin. Her eyes were searching him for answers.

"What can I demand?" he said. "He is my father. All that I have—all that *we* have—he has given us. He knows our needs. We live in his house."

"Yes," said Rachel. "We live in his house. You and I, two grown adults, living in your father's house like two children. And soon we will have our own child. It is time for us to be on our own, Simeon. Beyond time."

Simeon nodded. "He loves us, you know that."

"But he loves Reuben more," said Rachel.

"That's not true," said Simeon weakly.

"Isn't it? Then let him prove it. You are the elder son. By rights, you should have had your inheritance before Reuben. You would never have done what Reuben has. Why hasn't your faithfulness been rewarded?" Her face was red now with frustration, and Simeon could only nod his agreement.

Rachel looked at Simeon, sweaty and dirty from working in the hot sun, and her anger ebbed. Here he was, the most honest, hardworking man she had ever known, standing there with his head down, convicted of being faithful. Of being obedient. Of loving his father. Her heart softened, but the truth remained hard. "When does our life begin, Simeon?" she asked gently.

Simeon shook his head, at a loss.

Rachel reached out and took his hand, raising it to her cheek, her anger gone. Simeon was aware that his hands were dirty and would mar her beauty, but her warm skin felt good on his palm. Rachel closed her eyes and murmured, "We have been patient, my love. Our time has come. Do not ask Eli anymore—tell him." She opened her eyes.

He nodded sadly. "You are right, Rachel. It is time."

SIXTEEN

STORM CLOUDS

Reuben clenched his fists as he stomped down the street. "That damned Ahmad!" he hissed to himself. "I should have known!"

He had gone by Ahmad's home. The servant said he was gone. When Reuben said he hadn't seen Ahmad in several days, the servant simply shrugged.

"When is he returning?" asked Reuben, trying to remain calm.

"He didn't say," said the servant, frowning. "He left the city."

"What?" howled Reuben. "Why?"

"He didn't say," repeated the servant coolly.

Reuben had acted on impulse then, barging past the servant. He found himself in the great room of the house. It was empty of furnishings, except for a few pillows and tapestries. He gestured about. "What does this mean?"

"Master Ahmad is gone. I don't know where. Before he left two days ago, he dismissed us and told us to sell the remaining furnishings."

Reuben snatched up an embroidered pillow. The servant grabbed at it, and they stood there, each tugging on a corner.

"I want my money," said Reuben, hauling the pillow in.

The servant, a half-head taller than Reuben, pulled the pillow back. "It is mine."

"He owes me money," yelled Reuben, pulling the pillow.

The servant laughed. "He owes everybody money. Have you ever seen him work?"

Reuben clutched the pillow tightly. "I figured he was a wealthy man, like me."

"Like you?" sneered the servant. "Well, one of you is wealthy, now." He released the pillow and Reuben fell backward, hitting the marble floor hard, cracking his head.

"Now get out," said the servant, looming over Reuben. "Or I will call the Centurion."

Reuben went to Rahab's house. She, too, was gone, but he found her in the marketplace, discussing the price of walnuts with a merchant.

"Rahab," he yelled.

She turned, and as he approached, he saw her face change from pleasure to steeled emptiness.

Reuben pulled her aside. "Ahmad is gone," he moaned.

"So?" said Rahab, holding a handful of walnuts.

"So? He took all my money!"

"What do you mean, *all* your money?"

Reuben shook his head. "An investment. In precious stones. He took my money."

Rahab shrugged. "He'll be back."

"His house is empty. All I got was this." He held up the embroidered pillow.

Rahab laughed. "Then even as a poor man, you'll sleep comfortably." She turned back to the merchant.

Reuben grabbed her arm. "I have no money," he repeated.

Rahab pulled her arm away. "Neither do I."

"But I've given you a thousand drachmas if I've given you one."

Rahab held up a coin. "And here is the one," she said, handing the coin to the merchant and putting the walnuts in her bag. "Now I'm as destitute as you," she said, batting her golden eyelids and reaching into the bag. "Here. Have a walnut."

———•◦•———

All day, Reuben went from friend's house to friend's house but was turned away each time. When word got out he was penniless, they even quit answering the doors. He returned to his house and sat on the steps. When the head servant returned, he found Reuben on the granite steps, holding his head in his hands, weeping. "Master Reuben, what is it?"

"I'm lost, Gershom. Lost."

"What have you lost, sir?"

Reuben looked up at the old man. "My money. All of it."

Gershom took a step back. "But you haven't paid us this month!"

Reuben shook his head, waving Gershom away.

"But we must be paid," insisted Gershom. Reuben wouldn't meet his eyes. After a long time the old man walked inside and shut the door. The bar was dropped with a loud clang, and Reuben shuddered. A few minutes later, a cloak wafted down from the upper story and landed beside him on the step. He looked up. Gershom's face appeared in the window above.

"The rest we will sell for our wages, sir," he said emphatically.

Reuben looked up. He picked up the fine blue linen cloak, dusting it off. "Is this all you're letting me take?"

"Well," snorted Gershom, "we are not barbarians!" The shutters slammed closed.

Reuben sat down on the embroidered pillow. He folded the cloak in his lap and stared across the square. A score of people had witnessed the event, and they stood stock-still, watching Reuben, an actor in a tragic play. He buried his head in his hands.

SEVENTEEN

PATIENCE

Jeshua finally finished the slow work of cutting and planing the timbers. He laid them out across the sawhorses and was scribing them for the dadoes he would cut for the diagonal cross member so it would fit flush in the door. Dadoes of this sort were rarely used in Galilee; many considered them a fancy affectation, but Jeshua thought them a good idea, and he hoped Eli would agree. He wanted to build a beautiful, unique door for the old man.

Simeon was speaking with Eli at the dooryard gate. He'd been in the fields all day and was nearly the same color as the ground on which he stood. Eli was sitting on the stone wall, his head bowed, listening. Occasionally he would look up as Simeon pointed to the horizon, where their fields stretched. The crops were coming in full now, new green shoots of barley where just a few weeks ago there were only dark furrows in the dirt.

"We cannot wait any longer, Father," said Simeon loudly enough to make Jeshua turn. "Rachel and I have been patient. The crops are coming up and you have enough help. Please."

"Simeon," said Eli wearily, "now is not the time." He stood and moved slowly through the gateway, toward the house.

Simeon followed him. "Father! When Reuben took his inheritance before his rightful time, I said nothing."

"That was wisdom. Be wise now," said Eli, stopping at the well, motioning for Arah to draw him water.

"But he took my inheritance!" pleaded Simeon, his hands splayed outward, his voice reedy and tight.

Eli drained the ladle and waved Arah away. He turned to Simeon. "He did nothing of the kind, Simeon. Your inheritance remains."

Simeon looked around, shaking his head. "You're spending it!" He shot Jeshua an angry look. Jeshua was facing the other direction and didn't see the look, but he knew who Simeon was talking about.

"Rachel is nearing her time," stated Simeon flatly. "When does our life begin?"

Eli drew himself up to his full height. He was still half a head taller than Simeon. "You would start a household at the very moment your wife is about to bear your first child? Foolishness. Besides, you are needed here. The lull after the planting lasts only a few weeks and then the work begins again in earnest. The weeding, watering, and thinning. The spring has been hot and summer will be like an oven. The crops that look promising now will wither and most will die. Without your help, our harvest will be lean, Simeon."

Simeon started to talk but Eli cut him off. "Don't argue with me. It's true, your brother's selfishness has cost us dearly. It has been a hard season without his labor, and it will get worse. I have your best interests at heart—you and your family's. Your time will come, and when it does," he said, putting his hand on Simeon's shoulder, "you will receive all you deserve and more."

Simeon shook the old man's hand off and stomped toward the house, glaring at Jeshua as he passed.

Eli watched Simeon go, shaking his head. "Patience, my son," he said quietly.

EIGHTEEN

Shadow of a Doubt

Arah got up early and walked east to Reoboam's Hill, the highest promontory in the area. Before going, he'd filled all the water jars in the house and even those in the fields so he would not be missed for several hours. Jeshua said he would be late because he had business to attend to in Nazareth this morning.

That gave Arah the whole morning to attend to his own business. As he reached the summit, the sun was just peeking over the mountains, many leagues to the east. In their shadow, the Galilee Sea shone like a dark, wet stone. Arah sat down under a large sycamore tree, scanning the horizon. He'd never been out of Galilee, but he'd heard people say it was paradise compared to the rest of the world. He ached to see Jerusalem. Perhaps his prayers would be more effective if he offered them in the Temple. He could save and buy a pair of turtledoves and make a sacrifice. He would stand at the foot of the marble steps while the priest burned his offering in the bronze brazier, and he would pray, asking God about his father. Maybe God would hear a prayer offered in his own house, if he couldn't hear it out here in Galilee.

The rolling hills to the east were a lush green, dotted with forests and cut by roads, sloping down toward the Galilee Sea. A couple of years ago, Reuben had taken Arah and his friend Libni fishing on the lake. It was the biggest adventure of Arah's young life. They'd hired a boat and ventured out into the water. They had a small net, which they cast over the side. Reuben was an expert fisherman, and when he lofted the net into the air, for an instant it was a perfect circle hanging in the sky. Then it landed flatly on the water with a loud smack and sank quickly. Reuben yelled, "Pull!" and the three of them hauled the net in. Arah was astonished to see they had caught five silver fishes, but Reuben tossed them all back into the water. "Too small," he laughed.

"You mean there are bigger fish out there?" asked Arah, looking furtively across the water.

Reuben stretched his arms out as far as they would go.

"I don't believe you," said Libni, frowning. "You're a liar."

Arah was surprised at Libni's bold statement, but Reuben just laughed. "You're right," he said. "I am a liar. But I'm not lying about this."

For the rest of the day Arah listened to Reuben, wondering which things he said were true and which were lies. Reuben was handsome, smart, and funny. But his frank admission that he was a liar troubled Arah throughout the rest of the trip. Arah had once lied to his mother about doing his chores, but when he'd been caught his father would not speak to him for a week. His father's absence in Arah's life was so painful that Arah had vowed to never lie again. But here was Reuben actually boasting about lying. The idea that someone could be proud about lying was simply beyond Arah. So since that day, Arah had been wary of Reuben, even though he couldn't help but like the young man, who was always full of fun and energy.

Arah closed his eyes, remembering the haul of fish they'd taken back to Master Eli's estate that evening and what a feast they'd had—even the servants. And he remembered Reuben smiling at him, winking, as he picked his teeth with a fish bone. Arah was still confused, but months later, when Reuben left for Damascus, he found himself crying in the stable. He still thought about Reuben every day, wondering where he was and if he was all right. And wondering if he was still telling lies and getting away with it.

He closed his eyes. "Heavenly Father, how is Reuben? Can you see him from where you are?"

And, as Jeshua had counseled, he listened. In a nearby tree, a bird sang a short melodic phrase and the wind lifted Arah's hair off his forehead. He felt a shiver down his spine, but it was probably just the cool wind, not God's breath.

"I'm sorry to ask so many questions. Micah says I know too many. But if you'll just tell me about my father, I won't ask you any more."

Again he listened, feeling the suns on his face, remembering his father's sharp features and curly hair. Arah imagined his father with him in the little boat out on the Galilee Sea, watching as Arah threw the net far out into the water. His father nodded at him.

"What is it?" asked Arah, hauling the net in.

His father just smiled.

On the hillside, under the sycamore tree, Arah opened his eyes. He looked at the lake, now bright in the full sun. The hills beyond it rose dramatically, split by rocky outcrops and topped by groves of trees. You could probably see the entire Galilee from there. Maybe even the entire world.

"I'm trying to have faith," he said quietly, eyes not leaving the hills. "But it's hard."

The bird sang in the tree again. Arah stood and brushed off his tunic. He turned toward home and saw his shadow moving in front of him. He stretched his arms out like a bird, watching his shadow do the same. *Faith must be like my shadow,* he thought as he walked down the hill, his shadow slowly disappearing as he entered the hill's shadow. *Some days I have it, and some days I don't.*

NINETEEN

Mercy, the Robber

A week later, the door was near completion. The mahogany planks were sawed even, planed smooth, and joined together by top, bottom, and diagonal cross members dadoed into the red wood, flush with the planks. Jeshua had spent many hours sanding the wood to make it smooth. He had carefully drilled the holes for the new black iron lock, which was sturdy as well as beautiful. Tomorrow he would apply the finish with a fine horsehair brush he had bought from Azariah, a brush unlike any he had ever seen before, which came from distant Alexandria. Jeshua held the brush, feeling its balance, marveling at the smoothness of the bristles. Surely a brush like this would leave no trace of itself in the varnish. Eli would be pleased at such a luster.

He heard voices and turned to see Eli arriving on his fine black horse. Micah appeared and helped

Eli down. Eli then watched as Micah led the horse to the stable. Jeshua reached back into the toolbox for the brush. He wanted to show it to Eli, who would certainly recognize its value. The old man stood by the gate, looking to the horizon.

Jeshua approached him, the brush in his hand. "Master Eli?" he said.

The old man didn't turn. "What is it, carpenter?" His voice was deep and sorrowful.

Jeshua immediately forgot about the brush. "What is it, Master?"

Eli sat on the wall. He still looked to the west, where the orange sun was perched on the horizon. He sighed heavily. "How is the door coming?" It was question without interest.

Jeshua asked, "Master Eli, what troubles you?"

The old man sighed and said, "My friend Azariah has sent a message. He is far to the north and was in Damascus, where he again saw my Reuben." The old man's head wagged from side to side to dispel the unpleasant thought. "My Reuben," he repeated.

Jeshua put his hand on the old man's shoulder, but if Eli felt it, he gave no indication.

Eli continued, "He has lost all his money and his friends. Reduced to poverty, he is gleaning the fields for husks they feed to swine. My boy—eating what the swine eat!" He looked heavenward.

Jeshua expected to see tears in the old man's eyes, but they were dry.

"Perhaps you should go to him," suggested Jeshua.

Eli ground his teeth. Jeshua almost moved away from the old man, whose fierce temper he had seen before, but he kept his hand lightly on Eli's arm, waiting.

Finally Eli said, "I cannot." He glanced at Jeshua for a moment, then looked away. "Simeon is right. Reuben is no longer my son. He must be cut off. So says the Law."

"But mercy—"

"Mercy cannot rob justice," said Eli, pulling his arm away.

"Yet you love him."

"Yes," sighed Eli, lowering his head. "I do."

Both men sat quietly, Eli pondering the sunset and Jeshua looking at the brush in his hand. Finally, Jeshua drew a breath. The old man stiffened, prepared for an argument.

"Master Eli?" asked Jeshua. After a long moment passed and Eli didn't respond, he stood. "Nothing," he said, and started to go.

Eli's large gray head turned toward him. His jaw was set, but his eyes were pleading. "What is it, Jeshua?"

Jeshua stopped, his back to Eli. "It can wait."

Eli shook his head. "You were going to say something, young man. Say what's on your mind," he said plaintively, "as young men are wont."

Jeshua turned and faced Eli. "I have a question."

"Go ahead," said Eli.

"All right," said Jeshua, taking a deep breath. "I was wondering if you'd given any thought to the hinges." Eli furrowed his brow, but Jeshua continued. "Leather hinges won't support the weight of the new door. The hinges must be strong, so they should be made of iron, which can be oiled so they open easily. Above all, the door must open freely, don't you agree?"

Eli stared up at the carpenter and blinked.

"New hinges," coaxed Jeshua. "So the door opens freely . . ."

"New hinges."

"There comes a time," said Jeshua quietly, "when we must put away old things and embrace new ones."

"So I have heard," said Eli, shaking his head at his own foolishness. He should have known better than to think an uneducated carpenter would know a way out of his dilemma. He nodded and patted Jeshua's arm. "Whatever you wish, carpenter." Then he turned back toward the horizon and awaited the sunset.

TWENTY

The Welcoming Door

"Hold it steady, Arah," said Jeshua. "I've almost got it."

Arah struggled, pushing the door upward with all his might. Jeshua looked at the boy and smiled. "You don't have to hold it up, Arah, just hold it steady. We're almost there."

"But it's heavy," grunted Arah.

"And you're strong," said Jeshua around the pin he held between his teeth. "Now, just a little higher . . . higher . . . and . . ." He placed the pin in the slot and drove it home with a blow of the hammer. "There," he said, jumping off the footstool, grabbing Arah around the waist, pulling him deeper into the room so they could get a better view. "It's done."

The door hung motionless for a moment, then slowly began to close. "Look," said Arah. "It closes by itself." He beamed up at Jeshua.

"That's because the top hinge is set slightly toward the outside."

"Listen. It doesn't make a sound!" said the dark-haired boy in awe.

"That reminds me." Jeshua bent on one knee before the boy. "I have a task for you."

"Anything!" said Arah.

Jeshua shook his head, barely concealing a smile. "It's nothing grand, but it *is* important. *Very* important."

"What is it?" asked the boy, remembering the sweets the carpenter occasionally gave him.

Jeshua produced a small clay jar from his apron. It had a cork stopper in the top. He gave it to Arah. "This is oil for the hinges."

The boy's countenance fell. Jeshua wagged a finger at him. "You said 'anything,' didn't you?"

Arah nodded.

Jeshua looked up at the hinge. "The hinges and the lock are made of iron, and they are very expensive." He toggled the lock handle up and down. It moved smoothly and silently. "But to remain strong, they must be cleaned and oiled regularly. The first of every month."

The boy was looking at the vial of oil, his brow furrowed. "Every month," he repeated, committing it to memory.

Jeshua smiled at the boy's concentration. "Without fail. The door you and I built depends upon it." He took another step back, examining their work. The door, fully closed, fit snugly into the frame, not a bit of sunlight peeking through on any side.

Arah smiled. "We built a fine door, didn't we, Jeshua?"

Jeshua nodded. "Now, let's oil the hinges together. Next month, you will do it by yourself." He lifted Arah up, and the boy carefully unstopped the clay vial and deposited a few drops of oil on the door pin. Jeshua set him down and reached for the handle. "After you oil it, open the door a few times to work the oil in." He opened the door.

Eli and Simeon were standing on the stoop. Their faces showed surprise as the door opened. Eli nudged Simeon. "What did I tell you? It opens inward!"

Simeon looked doubtful as he stepped inside. Eli followed him as Simeon continued his inspection. Jeshua shut the door and stood aside as the two men considered his work.

"It opens inward," repeated Simeon, still perplexed. "A very strange idea."

Eli nodded at Jeshua, who said, "It opens inward to welcome friends and family—an invitation to share the comfort and hospitality of a fine home."

Eli ran his hands over the door. "I have never felt such a smooth finish," he said. "That brush you bought from Azariah really *is* amazing. This finish is flawless."

Jeshua winked at Arah, who grinned back.

"It ought to be," said Simeon, irritated. "It took him long enough. I thought he was building a ship out there."

"The finish protects the wood," said Jeshua, "against the elements."

They admired the door's deep red color. The planks and cross members fit snugly together. Eli ran his hands over the joints. "I can barely feel the seams."

"To last a long time, a door must be heavy," said Jeshua. "And because of its weight, it needs strong, flexible hinges. And the lock must be secure, now that the door opens inward."

Eli looked at Jeshua and chuckled. "Why, carpenter, that's more than you've said the entire time you've been here."

Jeshua smiled.

Eli clapped him on the back. "It's good to see a man take pride in his work. And even better to see that his pride is well placed."

"And what's this?" queried Simeon, pointing to a small rectangle in the door at eye height, a thin piece of mahogany that slid upward in two wooden tracks. "A window of some sort?"

Jeshua nodded. "Yes. A window." He grasped the small knob on the tiny shutter and raised it, letting in a narrow shaft of sunlight, which fell directly on Eli's chest.

Eli placed his hand on his chest, where the light fell. "It warms my heart, carpenter, to see such work," he said, unable to take his eyes off the small circle of light on his chest. When he looked up, there was brightness in his eyes as well, and he shook his finger good-naturedly at Jeshua, smiling. "You are quite a surprise, young man." He withdrew a coin pouch from inside his cloak and produced several coins, giving them to Jeshua. "You have earned this."

Jeshua nodded his thanks, then turned to the door. "Arah can tell you about the hinges."

The men turned and the boy gulped, surprised and shy. "Go ahead," said Jeshua. "Tell Master Eli about the hinges."

Arah held up the clay vial and said, "Iron hinges are strong, but they must be oiled. The first of every month." He looked at the ground, embarrassed.

Eli put his hands on his knees, bending toward the boy. "And you have been given this important task?"

Arah nodded.

Eli nodded. "So be it. Do not fail in your duties, Arah. We are depending upon you."

The boy looked up, surprised to be the center of attention. "Yes, sir," he said, nodding furiously. "Yes, sir!"

"All right," said Simeon, unmoved by the boy's enthusiasm. "Let's see these amazing hinges everyone keeps talking about." He grasped the handle, which slipped easily from the catches, and pulled on the heavy door, which opened without a sound. Simeon bent toward the lock, intrigued. "This is a unique mechanism, Jeshua—"

"Master of the Universe!" exclaimed Eli, clutching at Simeon's shoulder.

Simeon looked up, then followed Eli's gaze out the door. He straightened and squinted into the bright day. Far down the dusty road trudged a lonely figure. His head hung down, and he was dressed in rags. Eli took one step and grasped the doorjamb, holding his breath. In an instant, Arah was out the door, running toward the traveler. "Reuben!" he yelled.

Hannah, who was drawing water at the well, looked up as the boy rushed by, causing her to drop her water jar, which shattered into pieces. But her surprise turned to joy when she looked down the road. She grabbed her long skirt around her and ran toward the servants' quarters, shouting, "Master Reuben has returned! He's returned!"

Eli leaned against the doorjamb, afraid to move for fear Reuben would disappear. Simeon squeezed by him and stepped out into the dooryard. Across the road, in the fields, a number of servants straightened from their weeding, hearing Arah's yells. Micah got off his knees and began hobbling toward Reuben. Shouts of recognition carried toward the house. Eli turned to Jeshua, a question in eyes bright with tears.

"There is no justice, there is no mercy," said Jeshua quietly. "There is only love."

Eli grasped Jeshua with both hands. "Jeshua bar Joseph," he said, tears splashing off his cheeks and onto his tunic, "I now see what you have *really* been building here. Thank you."

Jeshua smiled. "Go to him."

Eli nodded and stepped into the dooryard. Jeshua had never seen the old man move so quickly. He strode by Simeon, clapping him on the shoulder as he passed. Eli soon made the distance to the low stone wall and easily jumped right over it.

Out in the road, Reuben, surrounded by servants, saw Eli coming. He broke free and ran. "Father!" he shouted. They met in the middle of the road, embracing and exchanging kisses.

Eli shouted, "Reuben! Reuben! My son! My son!" over and over. In an instant they were again in the midst of a crowd. From the fields and the house, more people ran toward the joyful reunion.

Only Simeon stood his ground, his hands on his hips as if he were made of stone. Jeshua walked over to him. Simeon glanced at him out of the corner of his eye. His lips were set in a straight line, and his eyes squinted into the bright sun.

"Someday you too may be lost and hoping to be found," said Jeshua gently.

"Never," spat Simeon. "I would never disrespect Father like he did." He scowled at the knot of people on the road, several of whom were dancing with joy. Eli, the tallest of all, turned toward the house and beckoned Simeon to join them. Simeon turned away, disgusted.

"Simeon, are you a righteous man?" asked Jeshua, a smile on his lips, remembering their exchange that morning so long ago.

Simeon shot Jeshua a hard look. He, too, remembered, and he quoted Jeshua: "The Lord will decide if I am."

"Well, I believe you are, Simeon."

"How would *you* know?"

"A righteous man respects his father."

Simeon crossed his arms across his chest. "So?"

In the distance, Eli still beckoned Simeon, who looked down and moved a foot, stirring dust.

"You have always respected your father. And you will respect him now," said Jeshua.

Simeon turned and looked at the reunion. By now there were twenty people in the road, but Eli's head towered above them all. While everyone moved buoyantly, Eli remained still, one arm around Reuben, but his face turned toward Simeon, his eyes hopeful. His other hand remained aloft, beckoning.

Simeon drew a breath, steeling himself. "For my father, then," he said, and started toward the road.

Eli's hand jumped up another six inches. "My son!" Eli exclaimed. "Simeon! My son!"

As Simeon walked slowly toward across the dooryard toward the road, Jeshua whispered, "It is a beginning."

He turned back to the house. The new mahogany door hung majestically on its sturdy black hinges. He took the handle and pulled the door toward him. It closed with a satisfying *thud*. He took off his apron, picked up his toolbox, and started toward the gate.

From behind him he heard a soft mewl and turned to see the little tan calf in its pen. He walked over to it, withdrawing a sweet from his pocket and holding it out. The calf came forward gingerly, took the sweet, and munched it with relish.

Jeshua remembered Hannah's remark about how Eli had been saving the calf for Reuben's return. "Some reunions are good-byes," said Jeshua, scratching the calf behind the ear.

Then Jeshua bar Joseph led his donkey through the gate in the low stone wall surrounding Eli's grand house and stepped into the road, turning west toward the Nazareth hills and home.

ᴛʜᴇ ᴄᴀʀᴘᴇɴᴛᴇʀ ᴛᴇᴀᴄʜᴇs

A few years later, Jeshua was conversing with a number of tax collectors and sinners, and his followers were dismayed that he would associate with such wicked people. But Jeshua, knowing the thoughts of their hearts, looked about at the people and opened his mouth.

And he said, "A certain man had two sons. And the younger son said, 'Father, give me my inheritance.' And his father did so. And shortly after, the younger son took his journey into a far country and there wasted his inheritance with riotous living. And when he had spent all of his money, there arose a mighty famine. And because he had no more money, he hired himself out to feed swine in the fields of a rich man. And because no one would feed him, he ate the husks that the swine ate.

"And when he came to himself, he thought, *Even my father's servants have more than enough bread to eat, and yet I perish with hunger! I will go to my father and I will say, Father, I have sinned against both heaven and you. I am not worthy to be called your son; instead, make me one of your hired servants.*

"And he arose and came to his father. But when he was still a great way off, his father saw him and had compassion, and ran and took him in his arms and kissed him. And the son said, 'Father, I have sinned and I am no more worthy to be called your son.'

"But the father shook his head and said to his servants, 'Bring the best robe and put it on him. Put a ring on his hand and shoes on his feet. Kill our fattest calf, and we will eat and celebrate! For my son was dead and is alive again; he was lost and is found.' And they began to prepare for the feast to celebrate the arrival.

"Now, during this reunion, the elder son was working in the fields, and when he came back to the house at the end of the day, he heard music and dancing. He asked one of the servants what these things meant, and the servant said to him, 'Your brother has come home, and your father has ordered a feast because he has returned safe and sound.'

"Now the older son was angry and would not go inside and join the feast. One of the servants told the father, and he came out and asked the son to join them.

And the older son said, 'For many years I have served you, and I have never disobeyed any of your commands. Yet you never gave me a feast that I might make merry with my friends. But as soon as your younger son returns—the son who spent your money on harlots—you make this great feast for him!'

"And his father said to him, 'Son, you are always with me. All that I have is yours. But it is right that we should celebrate and be glad, for your brother was dead and is alive again; he was lost, and now is found.'"

KENNY KEMP is an award-winning and best-selling author and filmmaker, whose memoir *Dad Was a Carpenter* won the Grand Prize in the 1999 National Self-Published Book Awards sponsored by *Writers' Digest* magazine. Shortly thereafter, he was signed by HarperCollins to write a multi-volume historical fiction series set in Judea at the time of Christ. In addition to his mainstream titles, he continues to self-publish and speak at writers' conferences, encouraging new writers to find a way to get published. When not writing, he works as a contractor, practices law, and flies his private plane.

Visit him at his website: *www.kennykemp.com*